PRIME CLIMB

Be careful as you climb this tree to grab the last apple.

Answer on page 47.

Illustrated by Paul Hicher

THE BIG ROUNDUP

29 breeds, types, and colors of horses and ponies are running loose in these letters. To round them up, look up, down, across, backward, and diagonally. Some letters may appear in more than one word.

Albino	Draft	Paint
Appaloosa	Falabella	Palomino
Arabian	Fell	Percheron
Bay	Galiceño	Peruvian Paso
Belgian	Gotland	Pinto
Chickasaw	Hackney	Roan
Chincoteague	Icelandic	Shire
Clydesdale	Midget	Thoroughbred
Connemara	Morgan	Welsh
Dales	Mustang	

```
C I D N A L E C I F O E C O T
W A S A K C I H C D S N L W H
Y C E M I T X I A S A P Y K O
N A O R N A J N U G P Q D N R
P H B I Z R I C R P N U E O O
A S A P P A L O O S A C S R U
L P E V B M M T C E I Z D E G
O T N I P E L E F L V T A H H
M N O L E N L A A A U E L C B
I N I T S N E G Y D R G E R R
N W I B T O F U I J E D R E E
O E W G L C Q E K A P I I P D
A L L E B A L A F X N M H S T
K S D N A L T O G N A T S U M
Y H A C K N E Y N A I B A R A
```

HUH?

Can you tell what's unusual in each scene below?

Answer on page 47.

STATE THE NAMES

Each pair of names here has a unique relationship. The first name appears in the capital of a state that is represented by the second name.

For example, the first Diana appears in InDIANApolis, which is the capital of InDIANA.

It's up to you to name the other capitals and their states. No letters are out of order or scrambled.

ex: __I__ __N__ DIANA __P__ __O__ __L__ __I__ __S__ , __I__ __N__ DIANA

1. FRANK __ __ __ __ , KENT __ __ __ __

2. ANNA __ __ __ __ __ , MARY __ __ __ __

3. HELEN __ , __ __ __ __ __ ANA

4. CARSON __ __ __ __ , __ __ __ ADA

5. __ __ LEIGH , __ __ __ __ __ __ CAROL __ __ __

6. HARRIS __ __ __ __ __ , __ __ __ __ __ __ __ VAN __ __

7. RICH __ __ __ __ , __ __ __ GINI __

8. CHARLES __ __ __ , WES __ __ __ __ __ __ __ __

9. __ AL __ __ __ __ __ __ __ __ __ , __ __ __ __ IDA

Illustrated by Barbara Gray

PICTURE MIXER

Copy these mixed-up squares in the spaces on the next page to put this picture back together. The letters and numbers tell you where each square belongs. The first one, A-3, has been done for you.

REVERE'S RIDE

Listen, my children, and you shall hear
Of the midnight ride of Paul Revere.
But Paul can't ride off so fast
Unless you order these pictures from first to last.

Illustrations by Marc Nadel

Answer on page 47.

HEROES

Four students, including Arnold, wrote essays about the following people: Clara Barton, Albert Einstein, John F. Kennedy, and George Washington. These four essays received grades of A+, A, B+, and B. From the information given, can you determine whom each student wrote about and what grade each received?

   Use the chart to help keep track of your answers. Put X in each box that can't be true and O in the boxes where the information matches. For example, clue 1 says the reports on presidents got the A+ and B+ grades. Therefore, you should put Xs in the boxes where the presidents' names meet the regular A and B grades.

	Barton	Einstein	Kennedy	Washington	A+	A	B+	B
Arnold								
Betty								
Connie								
Donald								
A+								
A								
B+								
B								

1. The two essays about presidents received A+ and B+ grades.
2. Connie, who did not receive the highest grade, got a higher grade than Betty.
3. Donald, who didn't write about Clara Barton, received a B.
4. The essay written by Betty was not about John F. Kennedy.

Answer on page 47.

MEASURE IT

We use many words to measure the things around us. 34 such words will fit into the grid on the next page in one unique design. Use the size of each word as a clue to see where it fits, and you'll experience a measure of success.

3 Letters
CUP
ERA
ROD
TON

4 Letters
ACRE
FOOT
HOUR
INCH
MILE
PINT
TIME
TROY
WEEK
YARD
YEAR

5 Letters
CLOCK
LITER
METER
MONTH
OUNCE
POUND
QUART
RULER
SCALE

6 Letters
GALLON
MINUTE
SECOND
SQUARE

7 Letters
SECTION

8 Letters
CALENDAR
DISTANCE
TEASPOON

10 Letters
CENTIMETER
TABLESPOON

Answer on page 48.

HIDDEN PICTURES

There are at least 16 objects hidden in this picture. How many can you find?

Illustrated by Judith Hunt

SAME STUFF

From the box at the end of each row, choose the one item
that belongs with the others.

Answer on page 48.

STOP, LOOK, AND LIST

Under each category, list one thing that begins with each letter. For example, one loud word that begins with "S" is Shriek. See if you can name another.

LOUD WORDS

S _____

C _____

N _____

W _____

L _____

SECTIONS OF A NEWSPAPER

S _____

C _____

N _____

W _____

L _____

SWEET THINGS

S _____

C _____

N _____

W _____

L _____

Illustrated by Lisa Dayer

Answer on page 48.

GONE FISHING

Put your line in and just relax. By using the clues as bait, you'll catch on to these answers in no time.

ACROSS

1. Sacks
5. Distant
7. Dressed in the latest style
8. Transportation charge
10. Grew older
12. Meat-eating fish
15. Genetic matter
16. Closed hand
17. Sunbathe
18. Solar fish
20. Exam
21. Soft powder
22. ___ for the course
23. Farther down
25. Russian ruler (anagram of star)

DOWN

1. Nighttime furniture
2. Morning (abbreviation)
3. Watery card game
4. Begin
5. Fishing pole
6. Historical period
7. Intended
9. Go in
10. Short form of advertisements
11. African antelope
12. Fishy astrological sign
13. Owns
14. Hardworking hill dweller
16. Strip of fish
19. Popular fashion
20. Old-time nickname for a sailor
22. For each
24. Ma's partner

Answer on page 48.

ROW, ROW, ROW

Each of the partygoers below is wearing a costume that has something in common with the two others in the same row. For example, in the top row across, each person has something green. Look at the other rows across, down, and diagonally. Can you tell what each person has in common?

Answer on page 48.

DOT MAGIC

Connect the dots from 1 to 75 to see a surprise.

GLOBE PROBE

That intrepid explorer Cincinnati Holmes has seen so much of this wide world that he sometimes forgets where he is. On these pages are some unique ways in which Cincy has viewed his maps. See if you can guess which country Dr. Holmes is visiting, as shown by the Xs on the maps. Look carefully. Cincy's maps all face different directions.

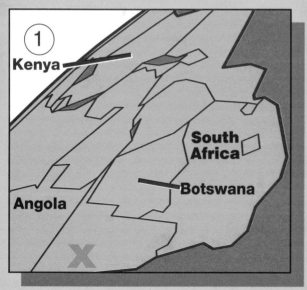

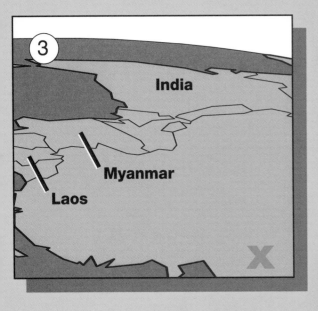

③ India
Myanmar
Laos

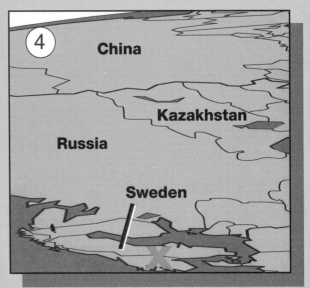

④ China
Kazakhstan
Russia
Sweden

⑤ Brazil
Bolivia
Paraguay
Argentina

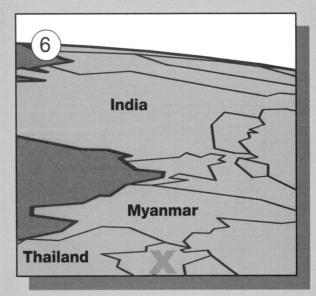

⑥ India
Myanmar
Thailand

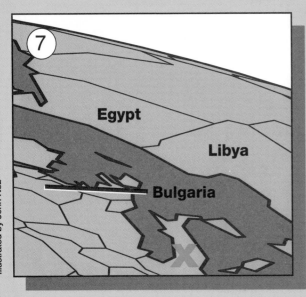

⑦ Egypt
Libya
Bulgaria

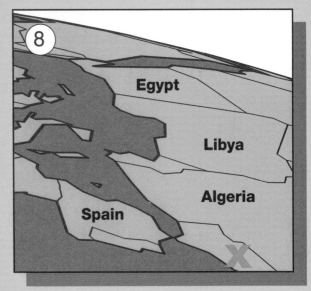

⑧ Egypt
Libya
Algeria
Spain

Illustrated by John Hinton

Answer on page 48.

WHO WROTE THAT?

Can you match the correct author's name to each book?

SEWING WITH THE NEW MATERIALS

TUMBLING MADE EASY

SNAKES OF THE JUNGLE

HOW I SOLVE BAFFLING MYSTERIES

SHOULD YOU RAISE WORMS FOR FUN AND PROFIT?

KEEP 'EM BLOOMING ALL SUMMER LONG

HOW TO RECOGNIZE THE CALL OF BIRDS

YOU CAN BE A WEIGHT LIFTER

WILD FELINES OF NORTH AMERICA

ALL ABOUT MANY-SIDED FIGURES

Jim Nast

Polly Ester

Violet Rose

Bob Katz

May B. Knott

Bob White

I. Guess

Anna Conda

Bea Strong

Polly Gahns

Illustrated by Gregg Valley

Answer on page 48.

WHAT'S IN A WORD?

Even the letters in a small word like PARROT can be moved around to form a lot of new words. Use the letters in PARROT to find each word below.

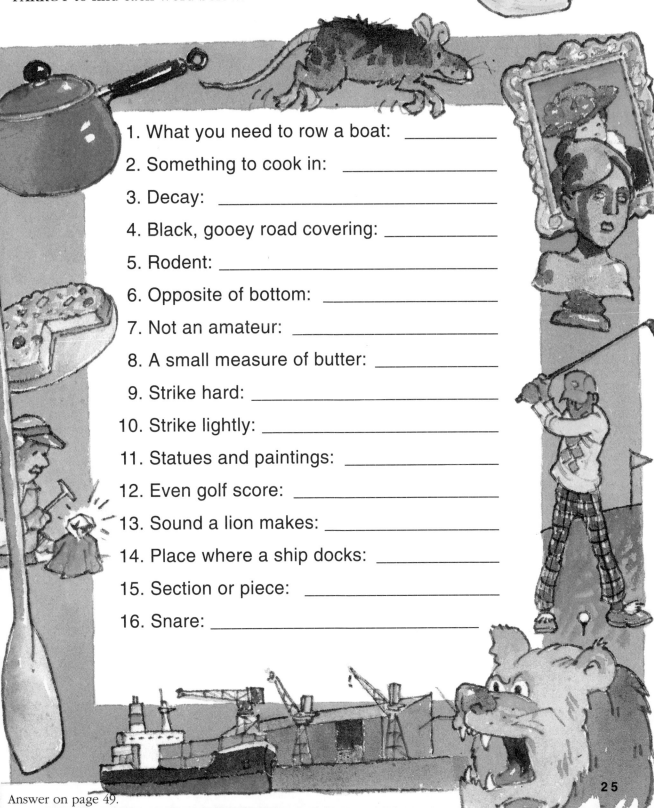

1. What you need to row a boat: _____

2. Something to cook in: _____

3. Decay: _____

4. Black, gooey road covering: _____

5. Rodent: _____

6. Opposite of bottom: _____

7. Not an amateur: _____

8. A small measure of butter: _____

9. Strike hard: _____

10. Strike lightly: _____

11. Statues and paintings: _____

12. Even golf score: _____

13. Sound a lion makes: _____

14. Place where a ship docks: _____

15. Section or piece: _____

16. Snare: _____

Answer on page 49.

A SHELL-TERED LIFE

Each number below stands for a letter of the alphabet. Use the code to identify these things that come in a shell. To get you started, the code numbers for each letter in A SHELL-TERED LIFE are given below. All code numbers are the same throughout the puzzle.

S=1 H=2 E=3 L=4 T=5 R=6 D=7 I=8 F=9 A=10

5-25-6-5-4-3-1

15-8-3-1

15-3-10-6-4-1

4-12-14-1-5-3-6-1

5-10-21-12-1

10-6-26-10-7-8-4-4-12-1

21-12-21-12-19-25-5-1

1-19-10-8-4-1

21-6-10-14-1

15-3-21-10-19-1

3-18-18-1

12-17-1-5-3-6-1

15-8-1-5-10-21-2-8-12-1

15-3-5-3-6   15-25-26-15-22-8-19—3-10-5-3-6-'1   13-8-9-3

Answer on page 49.   Illustrated by R. Michael Palan

MARCH MATCH

Match each streamer with the window where it unfurled.

Illustrated by Anni Matsick

Answer on page 49.

BILLBOARD BRAGGINGS

This empty billboard is waiting by the side of the highway. Put your favorite product or your favorite face on it along with some slogan. Use your imagination and have fun.

Illustrated by Jerry Zimmerman

NUMBER HUNT

First, solve all the equations below. Then look for the answers to be spelled out somewhere in the letter grid. Look up, down, across, backward, and diagonally. Some letters may appear in more than one word.

1. 36 + 14 = _____
2. 40 x 2 = _____
3. 22 - 18 = _____
4. 15 x 2 = _____
5. 40 ÷ 8 = _____
6. 42 + 12 = _____
7. 16 ÷ 8 = _____
8. 108 ÷ 9 = _____
9. 11 + 7 = _____
10. 32 - 24 = _____

11. 36 + 27 = _____
12. 44 - 38 = _____
13. 8 x 7 = _____
14. 12 + 40 = _____
15. 45 ÷ 5 = _____
16. 39 - 16 = _____
17. 12 x 7 = _____
18. 83 - 52 = _____
19. 34 ÷ 2 = _____
20. 50 - 39 = _____

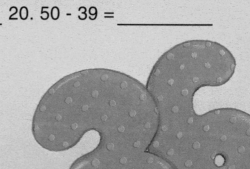

Illustrated by Sherry Neidigh

```
F I F T Y F O U R K L N E
E I O K E I G H T Y G L D
S V F W Y F Y T K G E P E
E S I T T T C G W V D E I
E I L F Y Y J F E E R S G
N X G N E S T N M H L E H
O T M H C I R F T W O V T
Y Y L M T X G Y I S T E E
T T Y X J Y T H X F B N E
R H R C S N F Y T K Y T N
I R L I E N F O U R Z E I
H E X W H D P D U H F E N
T E T J Y T D C G R C N E
```

Answer on page 49.

OWL FIND YOU

How many owls are hiding in this picture?

THE MESSAGE IS GARBLED

Each of these words features the letters GAR. Use the descriptions to figure out the rest of the words.

1. A style of dress: GAR __

2. Automobiles are parked here: GAR __ __ __

3. Flowers and vegetables grow here: GAR __ __ __

4. To rinse the throat: GAR __ __ __

5. Strong-scented bulb used in cooking: GAR __ __ __

6. January birthstone: GAR __ __ __

7. Harmless snake with yellow stripes: GAR __ __ __

8. Trash: GAR __ __ __ __

9. Wreath of flowers: GAR __ __ __ __

10. Article of clothing: GAR __ __ __ __

11. On a building, a grotesque carving: GAR __ __ __ __ __

12. Fragrant flower: GAR __ __ __ __ __

Answer on page 49.

33

UNDERGROUND EXPLORERS

You'll dig up the answer to the question below if you follow these directions. Find the letters asked for in each statement and place them in the number positions. All spaces marked with the same numbers get the same letters. Keep your eyes open and your head down as you search for the answer.

What did the cave explorer wear to her ballet recital?

__ __ __ __ __ __ - __ __ __ __ __ __
1   2   3   4   3   5   2   6   7   8   2   1

- The bats are hanging around in front of letter six.
- Letter five can be found among the wall drawings.
- Letter eight is in among the stalagmites.
- The lake holds letter four.
- One of the explorers is wearing letter seven on his or her helmet.
- Find letter one swirling in stone.
- Letter three is dripping from the ceiling.
- Look at a rock bottom to find letter two.

Answer on page 49.

HOUSE ABOVE

How many differences can you see between these two pictures?

Illustrated by John Nez

INSTANT PICTURE

You'll really be cooking once you fill in each space with two dots.

Illustrated by Jeff Stahler

SEEING STARS

Each of the definitions below calls for a word or phrase containing the word STAR. (Some are proper names.) Are you "star bright" enough to identify all of them?

1. It guided the Magi to the manger.

2. Francis Scott Key wrote it.

3. Common name for Sirius, which follows the constellation Orion

4. Promising young movie actress

5. Another name for a meteor

6. Nautical word for right-hand side of a ship

7. Symbol of Judaism

8. The Beatles' drummer

9. Another word for daydreaming

10. Nickname for Texas

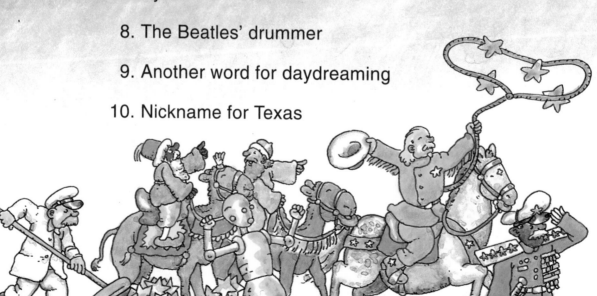

11. A planet, especially Venus, that rises in the east shortly before the sun

12. Winning quarterback in the first two Super Bowls

13. A general of the U.S. Army wears this insignia.

14. Popular name for the anti-nuclear missile system, Strategic Defense Initiative, or movie with R2-D2 and C-3PO

15. Another name for Polaris, the bright star in the Little Dipper

16. The first artificial satellite for global communication, launched in 1962

17. To be grateful for your good fortune

18. Woman reporter of comic strip fame

Illustrated by Charles Jordan

Answer on page 49.

LETTER LINES

This puzzle is not as complicated as it looks. Just follow the arrows from box to box, placing the same letter in each connected box. Some starting letters are already given, while some other letters need to be guessed. The more letters you fill in, the easier it gets. When you're finished, you should be able to read a fun fact.

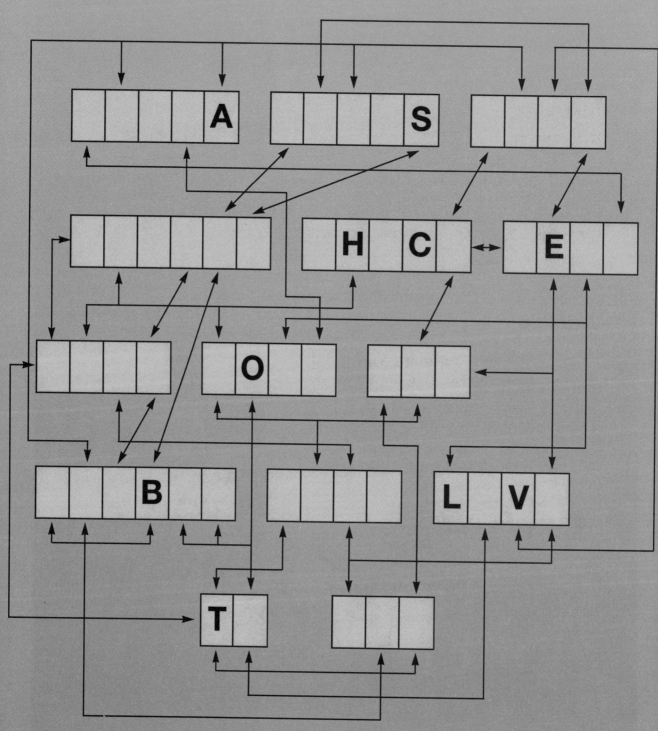

Answer on page 49.

Take a long look at this picture. Try to remember everything you see in it. Then turn the page and try to answer some questions without looking back.

DON'T READ THIS UNTIL YOU HAVE LOOKED AT "Smootzie Memories—Part 1" ON PAGE 41.

SMOOTZIE MEMORIES   Part 2

Can you answer these questions about the scene you saw? Don't peek!

1. What design was on the curtains?
2. What type of animal was the Smootzie?
3. What color was the Smootzie's beak?
4. What adjective described the Smootzie?
5. What does the Smootzie like to eat?
6. How many tail feathers did the Smootzie have?
7. What letter was on the explorer's pocket?
8. What color was the explorer's tie?
9. What type of hat was the explorer wearing?

Answer on page 50.

MAKING MONEY

You just got a part-time job for three weeks (15 working days). But you have to make a choice as to how to be paid. Do you want to make $10.00 every day, *or* would you prefer to be paid one cent the first day you work, two cents the second day, and each day thereafter be paid double what you made the previous day? It does make a difference.

Answer on page 50.

MAYAN MAZE

This mighty maze was discovered in some Mayan ruins. Will you be the first explorer to find a way out?

Answer on page 50.

YARD SALE

This yard sale is filled with great stuff. But how many objects can you find that have only three letters in their names? There's a cat and at least 25 other items.

Illustrated by John Nez

DOG DAZE

These dogs are unsure of where to go because a cat has scrambled the names on each house. Help these dogs by unscrambling the name of each breed.

8 INTOPER

7 OLLICE

6 ROBEX

5 RETIRER

4 BAGLEE

3 STREET

2 DELOOP

1 PLANSIE

Illustrated by Anni Matsick

Answer on page 50.

ANSWERS

PRIME CLIMB (page 3)

THE BIG ROUNDUP (pages 4-5)

HUH? (page 6)

1. Oranges grow on trees, not on the ground.
2. Dogs can't sweat.
3. Birds have no feathers when they hatch.
4. The Barber Shop sign is backward.

STATE THE NAMES (page 7)

1. Frankfort, Kentucky
2. Annapolis, Maryland
3. Helena, Montana
4. Carson City, Nevada
5. Raleigh, North Carolina
6. Harrisburg, Pennsylvania
7. Richmond, Virginia
8. Charleston, West Virginia
9. Tallahassee, Florida

PICTURE MIXER (pages 8-9)

REVERE'S RIDE (page 10)

4 6
5 2
1 3

HEROES (page 11)

Donald received a B and did not write about Barton (clue 3), Washington, or Kennedy (clue 1), so he wrote about Einstein. Neither Connie nor Betty received the A+ (clue 2); Arnold did, so Connie received the A and Betty the B+(clues 2 and 3). Connie did not write about Washington or Kennedy (clue 1); she wrote about Barton. Betty did not write about Kennedy (clue 4); she wrote about Washington. Arnold wrote about Kennedy.

In Summary -
Arnold - Kennedy - A+   Betty - Washington - B+
Connie - Barton - A   Donald - Einstein - B

MEASURE IT (pages 12-13)

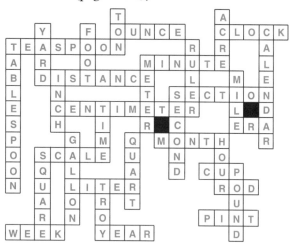

SAME STUFF (page 16)
1. C - Arrow pointing down
2. C - A microscope makes things look bigger.
3. A - Street sign
4. B - Mammal
5. A - Measures things with numbers

STOP, LOOK, AND LIST (page 17)
Here are our answers. You may have found others.

LOUD WORDS

Shout	Wail
Cry	Laugh
Noise	

SECTIONS OF A NEWSPAPER

Sports	Weather
Comic	Listings
News	

SWEET THINGS

Sugar	Watermelon
Caramel	Lollipop
Nougat	

GONE FISHING (pages 18-19)

ROW, ROW, ROW (page 20)

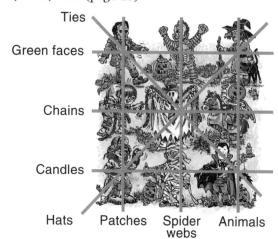

Ties
Green faces
Chains
Candles
Hats   Patches   Spider webs   Animals

DOT MAGIC (page 21)

GLOBE PROBE (pages 22-23)

1-Namibia	5-Uruguay
2-Canada	6-Laos
3-China	7-Italy
4-Norway	8-Morocco

WHO WROTE WHAT? (page 24)

Sewing with the New Materials — Jim Nast
Tumbling Made Easy — Polly Ester
Snakes of the Jungle — Violet Rose
How I Solve Baffling Mysteries — Bob Katz
Should You Raise Worms for Fun and Profit? — May B. Knott
Keep 'Em Blooming All Summer Long — Bob White
How to Recognize the Call of Birds — I. Guess
You Can Be a Weight Lifter — Anna Conda
Wild Felines of North America — Bea Strong
All About Many-Sided Figures — Polly Gahns

WHAT'S IN A WORD? (page 25)

1. oar	5. rat	9. rap	13. roar
2. pot	6. top	10. tap	14. port
3. rot	7. pro	11. art	15. part
4. tar	8. pat	12. par	16. trap

A SHELL-TERED LIFE (pages 26-27)

TURTLES
PIES
PEARLS
LOBSTERS
TACOS
ARMADILLOS
COCONUTS
SNAILS
CRABS
PECANS
EGGS
OYSTERS
PISTACHIOS
PETER PUMPKIN-EATER'S WIFE

MARCH MATCH (page 28)

A-1   B-2   C-4   D-3

NUMBER HUNT (pages 30-31)

1. Fifty	11. Sixty-three
2. Eighty	12. Six
3. Four	13. Fifty-six
4. Thirty	14. Fifty-two
5. Five	15. Nine
6. Fifty-four	16. Twenty-three
7. Two	17. Eighty-four
8. Twelve	18. Thirty-one
9. Eighteen	19. Seventeen
10. Eight	20. Eleven

THE MESSAGE IS GARBLED (page 33)

1. garb	5. garlic	9. garland
2. garage	6. garnet	10. garment
3. garden	7. garter	11. gargoyle
4. gargle	8. garbage	12. gardenia

UNDERGROUND EXPLORERS (pages 34-35)

What did the cave explorer wear to her ballet recital?
STALAC-TIGHTS

INSTANT PICTURE (page 37)

SEEING STARS (pages 38-39)

1. Star of Bethlehem	10. The Lone Star State
2. "The Star-Spangled Banner"	11. Morning star
	12. Bart Starr
3. Dog star	13. Four stars
4. starlet	14. Star Wars
5. shooting star	15. North star
6. starboard	16. Telstar
7. Star of David	17. Thank your lucky stars.
8. Ringo Starr	
9. stargazing	18. Brenda Starr

LETTER LINES (page 40)

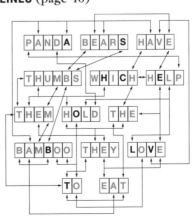

PANDA BEARS HAVE THUMBS WHICH HELP THEM HOLD THE BAMBOO THEY LOVE TO EAT

SMOOTZIE MEMORIES (page 42)

1. Stars
2. A bird
3. Yellow
4. Striped
5. Fruit
6. Four
7. A
8. Red
9. Pith helmet

MAKING MONEY (page 42)

The smart money takes 1¢ the first day and has the pay double each of the remaining 14 days. Here's what you would earn under that plan.

DAY	PAY
1	1¢
2	2¢
3	4¢
4	8¢
5	16¢
6	32¢
7	64¢
8	$1.28
9	$2.56
10	$5.12
11	$10.24
12	$20.48
13	$40.96
14	$81.92
15	$163.84

This adds up to a total of $327.67, which is a lot better than the $150.00 for fifteen days at $10.00 a day.

MAYAN MAZE (page 43)

DOG DAZE (page 46)

1. Spaniel
2. Poodle
3. Setter
4. Beagle
5. Terrier
6. Boxer
7. Collie
8. Pointer

Editor: Jeffrey A. O'Hare • **Art Director:** Jeff George • **Designer:** Glenn Boyd
Project Director: Pamela Gallo • **Managing Editor:** Margie Hayes Richmond
Editorial Consultant: Andrew Gutelle • **Design Consultant:** Bob Feldgus

Puzzle Contributors
Sal Agliano • Barbara Backer • Mike Carter • Patricia L. Dombrink • Susan Hall
Kathleen Pestotnik Iverson • Susan Keavney • Cari Koerner • J. David Lambert • Rich Latta
Isobel L. Livingstone • Thomas Mase • McKenzie Perrin • Clare Mishica • Joe Seidita
Verda Spickelmier • Holly Swisher • Kelly Trumble • Jackie Vaughan • Freddie Ware